THE BROONS AND OOR WULLIE

LET LAUGHTER FLOURISH

Mince and tatties, whisky and water, The Broons and Oor Wullie — these are all partnerships that have brought pleasure to Scots over many generations and their popularity shows no sign of being on the wane.

The artwork of Nottingham-born cartoon genius, Dudley D. Watkins, has kept a smile on the nation's lips since 1936, when Oor Wullie first appeared with his famous bucket and Maw, Paw, Daphne, Hen, Joe and the rest of The Broons Clan joined him in The Sunday Post Fun Section.

This book, the sixth volume of the collected antics of the residents of Glebe Street and that cheeky wee scamp Oor Wullie, brings together an hilarious selection of their adventures, whilst taking a light-hearted look at other rarities that are dear to the Scottish heart.

From Scottish Oscar winners to the Loch Ness monster and antique drams, they're all here — so read on and enjoy a <u>rare</u> treat.

FINEST SCOTCH WHISKY

Craig's

AULD AUCHENSHOOGLE

25 YEAR OLD MALT

70cle

PRODUCT OF SCOTLAND

BURNS

Printed and Published in Great Britain by D.C.Thomson & Co., Ltd., 185 Fleet Street, London EC4A 2HS.
D.C.THOMSON & CO., LTD., 2001 ISBN 0 85116 785 3

THE BROONS AND OOR WULLIE

The Sunday Post 15th March 1936

THE BROONS AND OOR WULLIE

The Sunday Post 22nd March 1936

The Sunday Post 22nd March 1936

The Sunday Post 29th March 1936

A RARE TREAT

The Sunday Post 24th January 1937

The Sunday Post 16th May 1937

A RARE TREAT

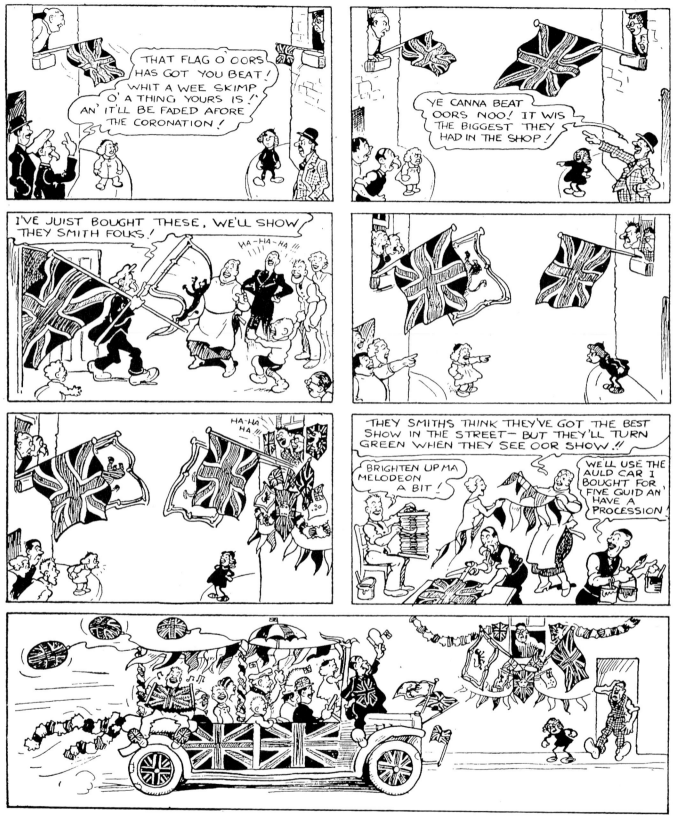

The Sunday Post 9th May 1937

THE BROONS AND OOR WULLIE

The Sunday Post 13th March 1938

HOT METAL MAGIC

A zinc plate of The Broons from the 1940s.

The finished print from the plate pictured above.

In the days before computers and the ultra-fast 21st century printing techiniques, metal plates were acid etched to produce a negative image of the original artwork. These plates were pinned onto metal mounts, along with any articles and type that completed the page. This page was covered with a papier maché mat and placed under a heavy weight, thus imprinting the raised lines of the plate into the paper. After this the papier maché mat was bent to fit the shape of a printing press roller and filled with hot metal. When this metal cooled it was placed on a roller and the printing of The Sunday Post could begin.

This was one of very few Oor Wullie stories to give a specific title to his adventures.

The Sunday Post 1st May 1938

THE BROONS AND OOR WULLIE

The Sunday Post 26th March 1939

A RARE TREAT

The Sunday Post 7th May 1939

THE BROONS AND OOR WULLIE

The Sunday Post 11th June 1939

The Sunday Post 24th September 1939

The Sunday Post 31st March 1940

The Sunday Post 25th August 1940

THE BROONS AND OOR WULLIE

A RARE TREAT

The Sunday Post 4th May 1941

THE LOCH NESS

Loch Ness covers 260,000 million square metres, is 23 miles long and 1½ miles across at its widest point. It is up to 754 feet deep and is the largest body of fresh water in Western Europe. Situated between the River Ness and the Caledonian Canal, it is surrounded by some of the most picturesque scenery in the Highlands, although none of this explains the loch's enduring popularity and worldwide fame.

That fame is down to the presence, or lack of presence, of Nessie, the monster that is said to inhabit the loch. The first mention of Nessie dates back to 565 AD when St Columba is said to have chased a "sea" or "water" monster back into the loch. There is also a story of a large animal coming ashore in 1572 and killing three people. More recently, in 1933, a visiting Londoner and his wife saw a long "trunk-like"

MONSTER

object cross the road in front of their car and disappear into the loch. Since that date there have been over 3000 reported sightings.

What exactly is it that people are seeing? Some say it is a plesiosaur, a type of long-necked marine dinosaur, that has long been thought to be extinct, while others reckon it to be a creature as yet unknown to science. In order for a population of monsters to be viable, there would need to be at least 14 individual Nessies living in family groups in different parts of

the loch. The amount of peat that is washed into the loch means that below a depth of 30 feet visibility is nil and, given that the average depth of water is 430 feet, there is plenty of room for these creatures to remain in hiding.

Sceptics, of which there are many, suggest that monster sightings can variously be explained by large eels, swimming deer, otters, sturgeon or floating logs. Various sonar sweeps of the loch have made "contact" with large objects at considerable depths but, so far,

their origins have remained unexplained.

Whether Nessie is fact or fiction, the very suggestion of her existence brings millions of pounds into the local economy, with upwards of 250,000 tourists visiting the permanent exhibition at Drumnadrochit every year. With the explosion of internet sites currently available, cyber Nessie fans can keep themselves up to date with events at the loch on-line, at www.lochness.scotland.net.

THE BROONS AND OOR WULLIE

The Sunday Post 15th February 1942

The Sunday Post 8th November 1942

The Sunday Post 18th April 1943

The Sunday Post 4th April 1943

The Sunday Post 16th May 1943

The Sunday Post 23rd May 1943

The Sunday Post 19th September 1943

The Sunday Post 30th May 1943

The Sunday Post 3rd October 1943

The Sunday Post 2nd January 1944

The Sunday Post 9th January 1944

THE OSPREY

The osprey, that beautiful black and white fish hawk, was once extinct in Scotland, with the last pair having disappeared by 1916. This was mainly due to persecution by man, with these magnificent birds being shot for their skins, which were then stuffed. As they became rarer their eggs became highly prized by collectors, which hastened their demise.

Unlike sea eagles on the west coast, ospreys weren't re-introduced, but returned on their own in the mid to late 1950s and were immediately given protected status. As a few pairs became established, artificial nests were erected to encourage the birds. The first pair at Loch Garten raised a brood in 1959.

A migratory bird, the osprey winters in West Africa before returning to Scotland, from late April onwards, to take advantage of the long summer daylight hours in which to fish and provide for the chicks. The male fishes for the entire family and when the catch is brought to the nest, the female rips it up and feeds it to the youngsters. The normal clutch is between one and three eggs with two being the most common.

Even in these more enlightened times, egg thefts are still a problem and an average of six nests are lost every season. Eggs are collected for collecting's sake, as they do not have any monetary value and for every egg taken one osprey is denied the chance of life.

Fortunately, the majority of people prefer to see the live birds and over 50,000 people visit the Loch Garten reserve every year, during the four month breeding season. Visitors are restricted to hides and are provided with binoculars and telescopes to view the birds. There is even a live TV link with close-circuit TV being installed in a

neighbouring tree in 1989.

Despite the problems, and with the help of dedicated wardens, the osprey's return to Scotland has been a success story. From the first returning pairs in the 1950s, numbers have increased dramatically and currently there are over 100 pairs nesting across the country, in such diverse locations as Caithness and Sutherland, Inverness-shire, Argyll, Tayside and Perthshire.

The Sunday Post 7th May 1944

The Sunday Post 13th February 1944

The Sunday Post 23rd July 1944

The Sunday Post 12th March 1944

The Sunday Post 10th December 1944

The Sunday Post 22nd July 1945

The Sunday Post 26th August 1945

The Sunday Post 14th October 1945

The Sunday Post 16th September 1945

The Sunday Post 28th October 1945

This song first appeared in the 1951 Broons annual.

THE BROONS' Family Album

(To the tune "SCOTS WHA HAE.")

Scots wha hae their hames in toons—
Hielan'men and country loons—
A' maun chuckle at "The Broons,"
    Scotland's family.

Gran'paw, young at eighty-six—
The Bairn, sae sweet, yet fu' o' tricks—
Maggie (she's the one for clicks!).
    What a family!

Pawky Paw, the family head,
Wi' Maw, the bonny lass he wed,
Though often trauchled, still are gled
    O' their family.

There's Hen, wi' every hair in place,
And Joe, the he-man lassies chase—
While Daphne has the homely face
    O' the family!

At the rest now hae a look—
Horace, nose-deep in a book—
The twins, like ane anither's spook!
    Complete the family.

That's the lot at No. 10—
Turn the page an' come on ben.
Every face ye're bound tae ken,
    For they're just YOU an' ME!!

A RARE TREAT

The Sunday Post 18th November 1945

THE BROONS AND OOR WULLIE

The Sunday Post 13th January 1946

THE BROONS AND OOR WULLIE

The Sunday Post 3rd February 1946

The Sunday Post 5th May 1946

THE BROONS AND OOR WULLIE

THE BROONS AND OOR WULLIE

The Sunday Post 24th March 1946

The Sunday Post 30th June 1946

THE BROONS AND OOR WULLIE

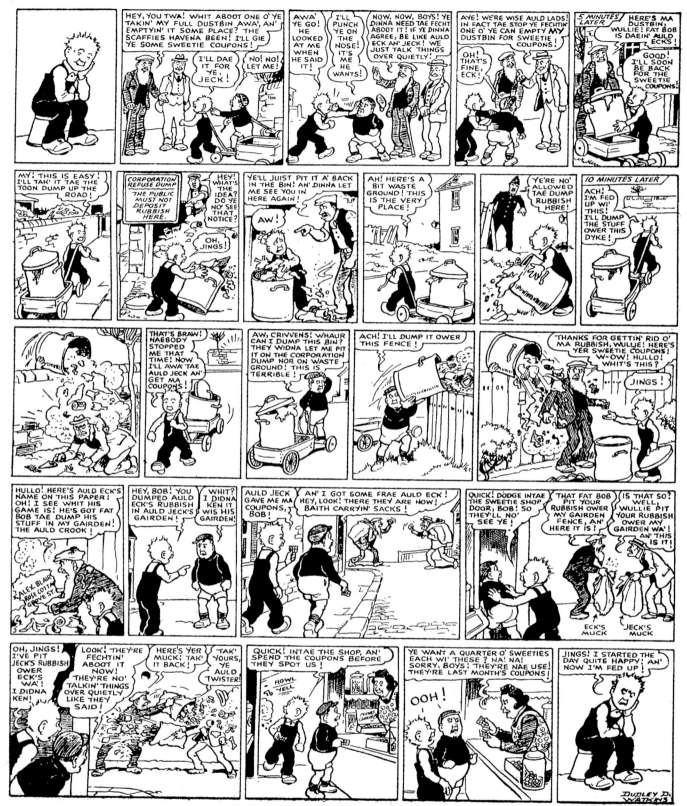

The Sunday Post 26th January 1947

The Sunday Post 2nd March 1947

THE BROONS AND OOR WULLIE

The Sunday Post 23rd March 1947

The Sunday Post 15th June 1947

WHISKY

Whisky, from the Gaelic "uisge beatha" meaning "water of life", has been Scotland's national drink for as long as anyone can remember and could hardly be considered a rarity. Indeed, there are distilleries the length and breadth of the country where the alcohol produced by the fermentation of malted barley is distilled into whisky.

Initially as clear as water, the whisky is matured in oak sherry casks and it is from these that the distinctive amber colour is obtained. (Several years ago, one distillery experimented with rum casks, instead of the traditional sherry casks, and the resulting cratur was a beautiful shade of green!) From the characteristic peaty malts of Islay to the sweetly smooth ones

of Speyside, every whisky brand is freely available — although there is a notably rare exception.

As late as 1994, in a way that would have delighted Granpaw Broon had it happened at the but 'n' ben, crofters on the Hebridean island of Eriskay were still digging up bottles of whisky that had been hidden by their predecessors some fifty years before.

The bottles are believed to have been "liberated" from the steamship Politician, which ran aground on Eriskay on a stormy night in 1941. Hundreds of cases of the cratur, bound for America, were rescued by the kind-hearted islanders.

Many were hidden from the Customs and Excise men who arrived on the island to prevent the whisky from being brought ashore. The whisky rescued from the shipwreck kept islanders warm throughout the dark years of the war, when drink was in very short supply.

Some of the hiding places, including those still being discovered by the crofters, were forgotten. This incredible true story inspired author Sir Compton Mackenzie to write the novel "Whisky Galore". The book became a bestseller and was later made into a successful Ealing comedy starring Basil Radford, Duncan Macrae and Joan Greenwood.

In 1987 a team of divers recovered eight bottles of whisky from the hold of the wreck, which by then was 30 feet underwater and firmly embedded in the sand, and they were later sold at auction for more than £4000.

The Sunday Post 30th March 1947

The Sunday Post 6th July 1947

THE BROONS AND OOR WULLIE

A RARE TREAT

The Sunday Post 26th December 1948

THE BROONS AND OOR WULLIE

The Sunday Post 9th January 1949

The Sunday Post 6th February 1949

THE BROONS AND OOR WULLIE

The Sunday Post 27th February 1949

The Sunday Post 6th March 1949

The Sunday Post 6th March 1949

The Sunday Post 13th March 1949

THE BROONS AND OOR WULLIE

The Sunday Post 1st January 1950

THE BROONS AND OOR WULLIE

The Sunday Post 9th April 1950

A RARE TREAT

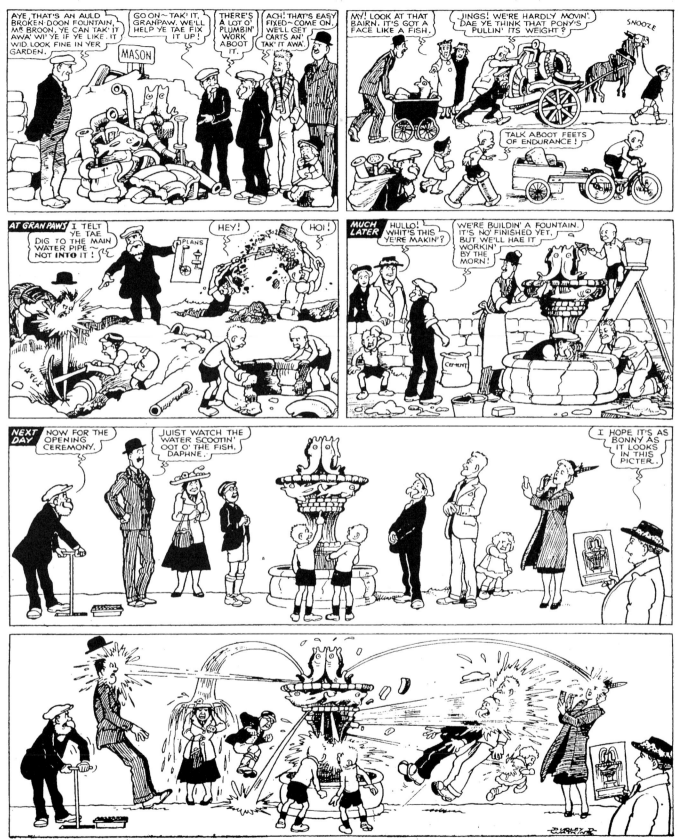

The Sunday Post 7th May 1950

THE BROONS AND OOR WULLIE

The Sunday Post 30th July 1950

A RARE TREAT

The Sunday Post 21st May 1950

THE BROONS AND OOR WULLIE

The Sunday Post 10th June 1951

The Sunday Post 18th November 1951

WINS AT THE

Although the Scottish football team has enjoyed success in qualifying for the World Cup finals, competing in eight of the sixteen finals held to date, the same cannot be said for its achievements in the later stages. Scotland have taken the field on twenty-three occasions for World Cup games and four times have we emerged victorious.

The first of our 'Fab Four' wins came in West Germany in 1974 when we defeated Zaire by two goals to nil, with goals from Peter Lorimer and Joe Jordan. Despite draws with Brazil and Yugoslavia, Scotland bowed out on goal difference — the only unbeaten team out of the 16 nations competing.

If the performances in 1974 had enhanced Scotland's reputation, those in 1978 in Argentina did not. Defeat by Peru, after Joe Jordan had opened the scoring, followed by a 1-1 draw with Iran, left Scotland needing to beat Holland by three clear goals to progress. Typically we came very close with our greatest World Cup win. Kenny Dalglish equalised an

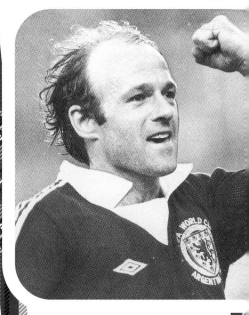

early Dutch penalty before Archie Gemmill converted another penalty. Gemmill then scored a breathtaking goal, twisting and turning past three defenders before lifting the ball over the goalkeeper. 3-1 and the dream was on! Sadly, or perhaps inevitably, Johnny Rep scored a 25 yarder and the 3-2 final score kept Holland in the tournament, where they went on to contest the

WORLD CUP

final with Argentina.

In 1982 in Spain, Scotland's opening game against New Zealand was duly won with goals from Kenny Dalglish, Steve Archibald, John Robertson and two from John Wark. New Zealand replied with two goals of their own, which would prove fatal to Scotland's chances. David Narey's memorable "toe poke" in the 4-1 defeat by the impressive Brazil, then Joe Jordan scoring for the third World Cup in succession in the 2-2 draw with Russia were other highlights as Scotland again lost out on goal difference.

Scotland qualified for Mexico in 1986, but we had to wait until Italy in 1990 for another Scottish win. After a disastrous 1-0 defeat by Costa Rica, Scotland beat a fancied Swedish team 2-1, with goals from Stuart McCall and Mo Johnston. A 1-0 defeat in our final game with Brazil sent us homewards tae think again.

So, there you have it, four famous Scottish successes in the World's greatest football tournament — let's just hope that these become less rare in the years ahead!

The Sunday Post 12th August 1951

The Sunday Post 23rd December 1951

The Sunday Post 22nd March 1953

The Sunday Post 29th March 1953

THE BROONS AND OOR WULLIE

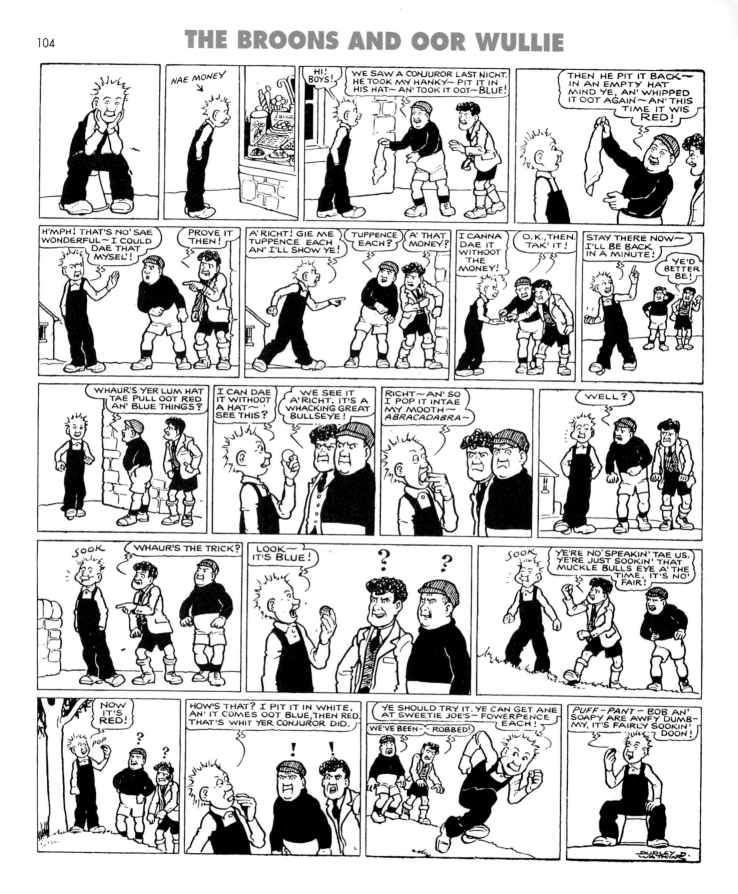

The Sunday Post 9th August 1953

THE BROONS AND OOR WULLIE

The Sunday Post 25th July 1954

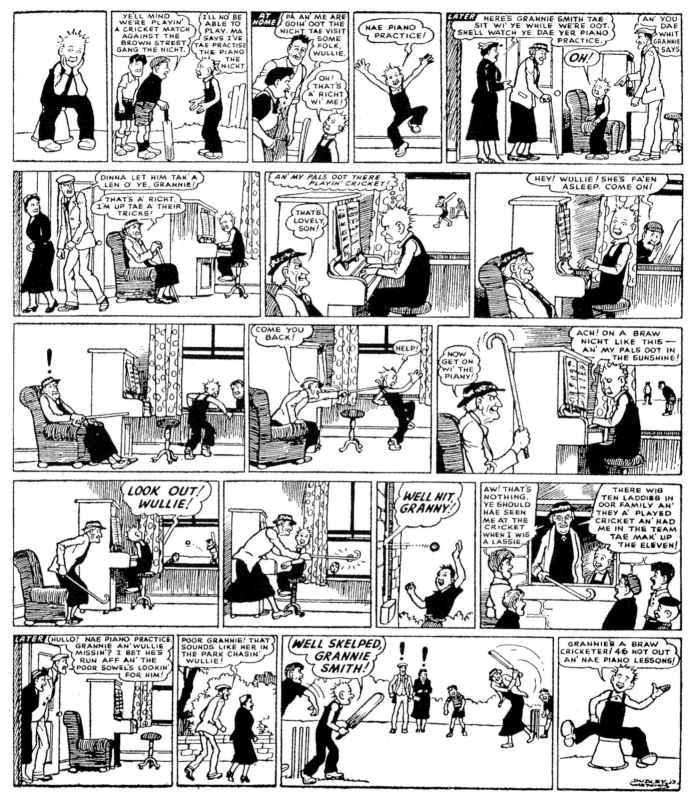

The Sunday Post 17th July 1955

The Sunday Post 1st January 1956

The Sunday Post 16th September 1956

What's a little laddie made o'?

This page first appeared in the 1956 Oor Wullie book.

WHAT'S a little laddie made o'?
Sugar an' spice? An' a' things nice?
That's no' what OOR Wullie's made o'!

What, then, is Oor Wullie made o'?
Towsy heid, an' dungarees —
Muddy boots, an' dirty knees.
Waggin' tongue that never ceases —
Jeelly noses, jeelly pieces.
Chewin' gum, an' bits o' string —
A catty that goes PING-NG-NGG!
Rabbits in hutches, tadpoles in jam jars —
Pretendin' he's drivin' upstairs in tramcars.
Laggin' feet when school goes in —
(Four o'clock, an WATCH HIM RIN!)
Pole an' string, an' bent-pin hooks —
Comics inside history books.
In summer, seven endless weeks —
O' picnics, freckles, torn breeks.
Come winter, sna'ba's, an' such tricks —
" Good anes," an' " bad anes " at the flicks.
An' last o' a', so his Ma's found,
A little finger tae twist ye round —
THAT'S WHAT OOR WULLIE'S MADE O'!

DUDLEY D. WATKINS

The Sunday Post 27th October 1957

The Sunday Post 24th November 1957

The Sunday Post 20th December 1959

The Sunday Post 20th December 1959

The Sunday Post 18th December 1960

The Sunday Post 17th April 1960

The Sunday Post 7th May 1961

The Sunday Post 12th November 1961

124

The Sunday Post 12th November 1961

The Sunday Post 26th November 1961

ACADEMY AWARD

For the 73rd time in March of this year, the Hollywood film industry rewarded those who work in it for standards of excellence in every aspect of film-making. These Academy Awards, affectionately known as Oscars, are regarded as the pinnacle of achievement for all actors as they are voted for by their peers.

Since the awards began in 1928, only three have so far been won by Scottish actors. The first Scot to pick up an Oscar was the renowned character actor Donald Crisp, who picked up an award for Best Supporting Actor in the quintuple

WINNERS

Oscar-winning film "How Green Was My Valley". This 1941 movie was directed by John Ford and told the moving story of a large, close-knit family of Welsh coal miners.

The next Scottish success came in 1958 when David Niven received the Best Actor statuette for his performance in "Separate Tables", an acclaimed drama set in a large hotel. His co-stars, Burt Lancaster and Rita Hayworth, played a divorced couple trying to make another go of things, while Kirriemuir-born Niven played a supposed war hero.

In 1987, former Edinburgh milkman, Big Tam Connery, now Sir Sean, after his knighthood in the year 2000, completed the trio of Scottish successes. After many memorable film roles in his long career, Connery finally won an Oscar for Best Supporting Actor in the film "The Untouchables". His compelling performance as a veteran street cop, showing naïve federal agent Eliot Ness, played by Kevin Costner, how to deal with Mafia violence and police corruption in Prohibition-era Chicago, was regarded as a tour de force.

Perhaps other Scots, such as "Trainspotting" actor Ewan McGregor, will join this elite group in years to come, although there is only one sure way to guarantee a future winner — extend the Academy Awards to include Scottish newspapers and there has to be a Best Supporting Actor award for Oor Wullie's bucket!

The Sunday Post 17th June 1962

The Sunday Post 25th August 1963

The Sunday Post 5th May 1963

The Sunday Post 23rd June 1963

The Sunday Post 26th January 1964

The Sunday Post 1st November 1964

The Sunday Post 7th March 1965

A RARE TREAT

The Sunday Post 14th February 1965

The Sunday Post 28th March 1965

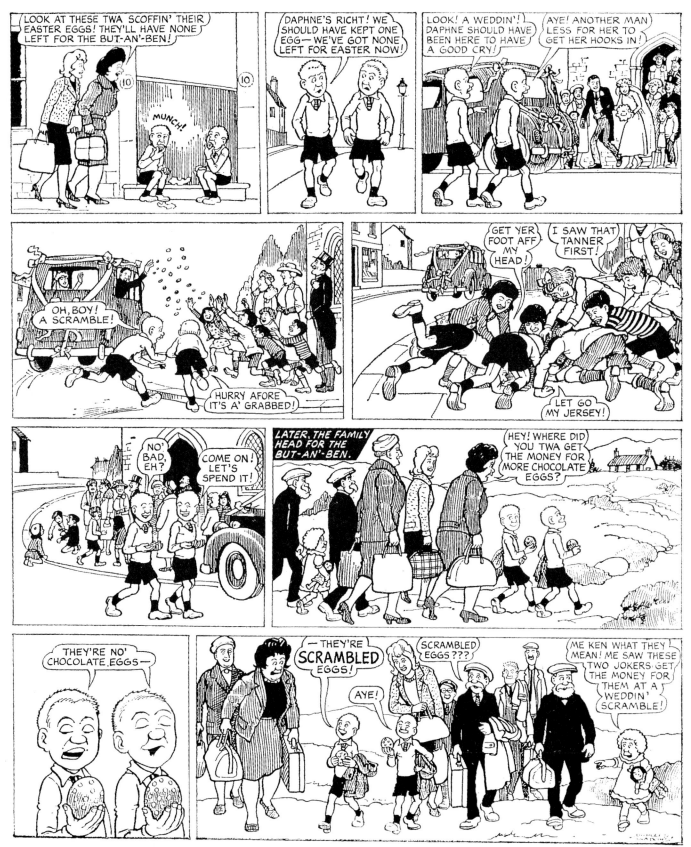

THE BROONS AND OOR WULLIE

The Sunday Post 25th December 1966

A RARE TREAT

FUNLAND

PUZZLES, TRICKS, GAMES & MAGIC

EVERYBODY'S PLAYMATE

★ BY ★ A.W. NUGENT THE WORLD'S LEADING PUZZLEMAKER

TRICK YOUR FRIENDS WITH THIS FREAK ARITHMETIC PROBLEM... ASK SOMEONE IF HE KNOWS HOW TO SUBTRACT 1 FROM 19 AND GET A REMAINDER OF 20.... HE WILL UNDOUBTEDLY SAY IT CAN'T BE DONE. THEN YOU WRITE DOWN THE NUMBER 19 IN ROMAN NUMERALS, XIX. STRIKE OUT THE NUMBER 1 (ONE) AND XX (TWENTY) IS LEFT.

SPRING

1 GRIN	2 SING	3 SIGN	4 SPRING	5
6	7	8	9	10
11	12	13	14	15
16	17	18	19	20
21	22	23	24	25

HOW MANY ENGLISH WORDS OF ONE OR MORE LETTERS CAN YOU FORM BY USING ONLY THE LETTERS IN THE WORD "SPRING." YOU ARE NOT PERMITTED TO USE TWO OF THE SAME LETTERS IN ONE WORD. DO NOT ADD "S" TO SINGULAR WORDS TO MAKE TWO WORDS... IF YOU CAN SPELL 25 OR MORE WORDS WE'LL RATE YOU AS AN EXPERT PUZZLER; FOR 20 WORDS YOU ARE GOOD; FOR 15 WORDS, AVERAGE; 10 WORDS, FAIR.

ARE YOU AN EXPERT PUZZLER?

3-22

A TINY CROSS-WORD PUZZLE

ACROSS
2 2,240 POUNDS
5 ADMIT AS A FAULT
6 TAVERN

DOWN
1 IMPRISON
3 A LIGHT PORTABLE BED
4 INQUIRE

NUMBER GAME DIRECTIONS. LAY THE SKETCH ON A FLAT SURFACE THEN TAKE TURNS, WITH TWO OR MORE PLAYERS, DROPPING A MATCHSTICK ON THE CIRCLES FROM ABOUT A FOOT ABOVE THE GAME. ADD ALL THE NUMBERS THAT ARE IN THE SECTIONS TOUCHED BY THE MATCHSTICK.

THE PLAYER WITH THE LARGEST SCORE AFTER 5 TRIALS WILL BE THE WINNER.

SVLOE YOYEEDBRV NRSGPI HET

TRY TO REARRANGE THE FOUR GROUPS OF LETTERS SHOWN ABOVE TO FORM WORDS... THEN REARRANGE THE FOUR WORDS TO FORM A SENTENCE.

A month after the first appearances of Oor Wullie and The Broons, on March 8th 1936, Fun Section readers moved into spring with this collection of puzzles. See if the passing of sixty-five years has made them any easier. Good luck!

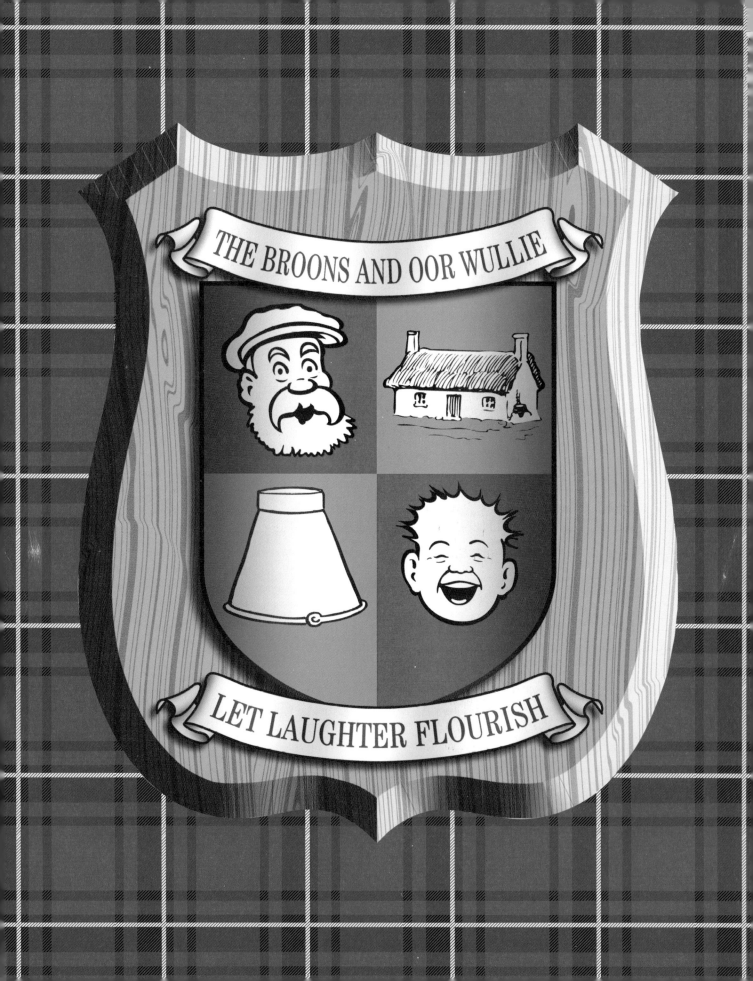